i AM

_____

By Jahkil Naeem

Illustrated by Sameer Kassar
Designed by Angel D'Amico-Bauer
Edited by Marti Parham

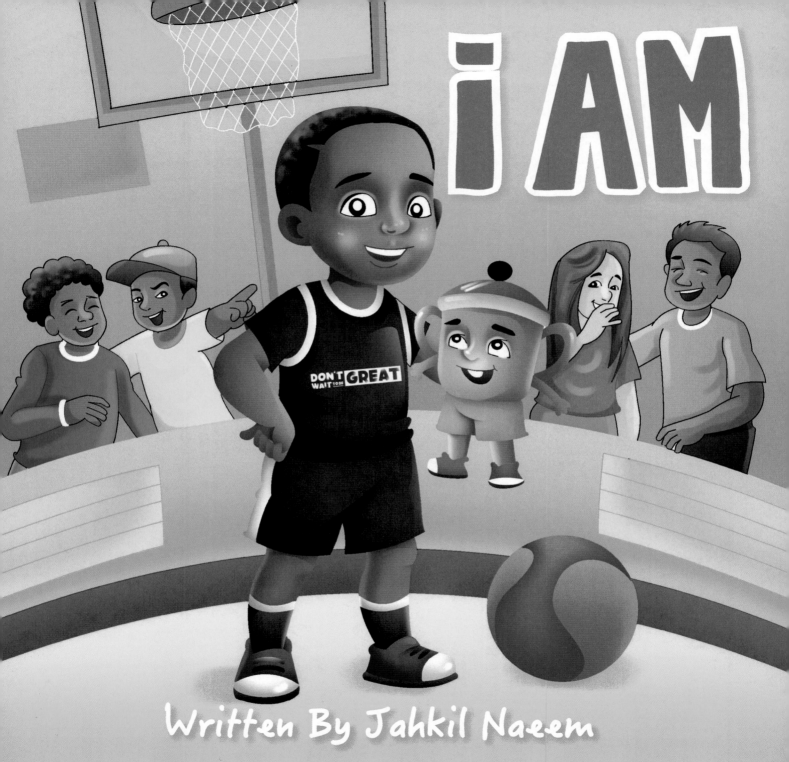

i AM

Written By Jahkil Naeem

This book is dedicated to my parents, grandparents, great grandparents, and my dog JJ. ☺

Special thanks to my book coach Mrs. Arriel Biggs.

Special note to youth everywhere: Remember, "Don't wait to be great!"
— Jahkil Naeem

Once upon a time, there was a kid who got bullied for being awesome.

He crossed over with ease, but often times got teased.

Jah felt the kids were mean, they said things that lowered his self-esteem.

He walked away with his head down, and his big smile became a frown.

He whispered to himself,
"This is the only place
I feel free to be me."

Six seconds on the clock,
he feels like he's
going to flop.

He shoots the ball and makes
the game winning shot!

His game winning prize came alive and became his encouraging friend for the long ride.

Jah told himself, "This trophy is the only one that knows me!"

12

Jah named the trophy John and all of his fears were gone.

John helped Jah throughout life, but it was a heck of a fight.

When he became grown,
he claimed his throne.

The bullies from before
became sad and alone.

They dressed, acted, and talked like him now, almost like a clone.

They now know not to treat people wrong.

Along the way, Jah realized
and told himself:

I AM a trendsetter,
I AM a go-getter,
A maker of change.
I have greatness running
through my veins!

So if you're ever in doubt,
remember to shout!

i AM BRAVE

i AM SMART

i AM HELPFUL

i AM FEARLESS

i AM COURAGEOUS

i AM POSITIVE

i AM HARDWORKING

i AM KIND

i AM THOUGHTFUL

i AM FUN

i AM AMAZING

i AM LOVED

i AM ME

Hey guys! Want to play a game?

STEP 1: Think of some cool words to describe yourself.

STEP 2: Think of what makes you that way.

Check out my samples:

I AM _kind_ **BECAUSE** _I like to help people._

I AM _brave_ **BECAUSE** _I am not afraid to stand up to bullies._

Sample Words:

Bold
Brave
Clever
Considerate
Cool

Dazzling
Friendly
Generous
Gentle
Giving
Good

Great
Happy
Important
Intelligent
Joyous

Kind
Nice
Outgoing
Quick
Sharp
Shy

Smart
Supportive
Unselfish
Valuable
Wonderful

Now You Try!

I AM _____ BECAUSE _____

_____

I AM _____ BECAUSE _____

_____

I AM _____ BECAUSE _____

_____

I AM _____ BECAUSE _____

_____

Can you think of one more?

I AM _____ BECAUSE _____

_____

About the Author

Jahkil Naeem Jackson is a social entrepreneur and founder of Project I Am, a nonprofit organization he created when he was eight years old. Now 13, Jahkil has a heartfelt desire to help those in need. Jahkil's mission is to build awareness of homelessness and to help the homeless population by offering "Blessing Bags," a giveaway filled with wipes, socks, deodorant, hand sanitizer, granola bars, toothbrushes, toothpaste, bottled water, and more.

In just a few years, Jahkil's efforts have touched almost 50,000 men, women, and children across the world. Along with the help of friends and family, Jahkil has organized distribution to those in need in Chicago, Los Angeles, Oklahoma, Washington D.C., Atlanta, Virginia, and Idaho. He has also provided Blessing Bags to orphans in Mbabane, Swaziland, as well as volcano victims in Guatemala, and hurricane survivors in Florida, Houston, Puerto Rico, and the Bahamas. During COVID-19, Jahkil hosted a virtual packing party with 40 youth from 28 different cities, creating 3,000 Blessing Bags.

Jahkil has been named a Youth Ambassador for Heartland Alliance, is a member of the WE International Youth Council, and has been acknowledged and honored by several major media outlets and most notably was named one of 2017's most influential people by President Barack Obama.

Even with all of his accomplishments, Jahkil has had to deal with his share of bullies. As a youth advocate he wants kids to stay positive and to never doubt themselves or their abilities.

Barack Obama ✔
@BarackObama

Ten-year-old Jahkil Jackson is on a mission to help homeless people in Chicago. He created kits full of socks, toiletries, and food for those in need. Just this week, Jahkil reached his goal to give away 5,000 "blessing bags." That's a story from 2017.

10-year-old's 'blessing bags' mission earns him national acclaim
5th grader Jahkil Jackson receives national award for distributing thousands of blessing bags to homeless people in Chicago
🔗 chicagotribune.com

10:10 AM · Dec 29, 2017 · Twitter for iPhone

44.8K Retweets   **1.2K** Quote Tweets   **289.5K** Likes

Barack Obama ✔ @BarackObama · Dec 29, 2017
Replying to @BarackObama
All across America people chose to get involved, get engaged and stand up. Each of us can make a difference, and all of us ought to try. So go keep changing the world in 2018.

💬 17.7K   ↻ 110.4K   ♡ 471.9K

Made in the USA
Monee, IL
05 October 2021